Teddy Bear Tea

Author: Ellwyn Autumn

Illustrator: Tanya Glebova

ISBN: 978-1-7354249-0-3

For Amos, my first Teddy Bear

Teddy told Rabbit, and Rabbit told me,

to meet them at three, for afternoon tea.

Rabbit said, “Pass the message on,”

and with a hip-hop, she was gone,

her fluffy white tail,

easing down the trail.

With a big smile on my face,

I quickened my leisurely pace.

Following Rabbit's command,

I took up the task at hand.

I wandered through the wood,

doing what I could,

to help spread the word,

until everyone had heard,

of the Teddy Bear Tea,

today, promptly at three!

As the time for tea drew near,

animals came from there to here,

from every lake, burrow, and cave,

in wave upon beautiful wave.

Chipmunks, deer, and snakes,

with berries, tarts, and cakes,

all came together beneath a tree,

with Teddy, Rabbit, and me,

for tea promptly at three.

It was a grand sight to see!

Under a sky of sweet baby blue,

we met friends who were honest and true.

In colors of black, brown, and tan,

we feasted, we danced, and we ran.

The party was happy and gay,
until night overtook the day,
and we could no longer stay.

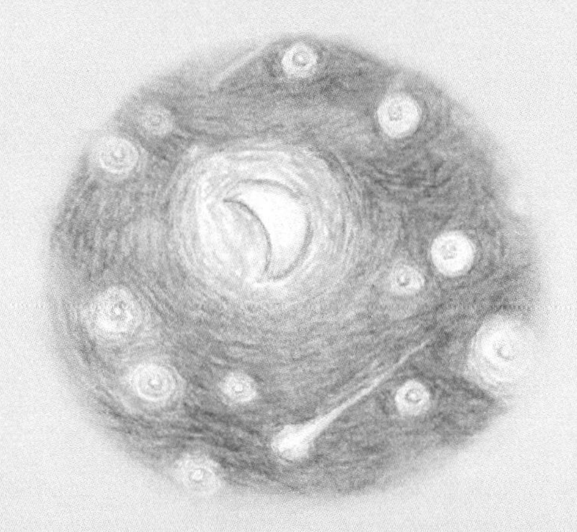

With happy hearts we gazed up at the moon,

knowing that we would see each other soon,

for yet another jolly afternoon,

of tea promptly at three,

with Teddy under the tree!

Teddy Bear History

On November 14, 1902, the beginnings of the Teddy Bear occurred when President Theodore Roosevelt refused to shoot a Louisiana black bear while hunting in Mississippi. It didn't take long for the incident to make national news and a series of imaginative events to unfold.

By November 16, political cartoonist, Clifford Berryman, got wind of it and satirized the episode in The Washington Post. Shortly after, Brooklyn candy shop owner, Morris Michtom, saw the picture and became inspired to create a stuffed bear that he named 'Teddy's Bear' and dedicated to the president.

Upon receiving President Roosevelt's permission to use his name for the toy, Michtom mass produced the bear and founded the Ideal Toy Company.

For further reading visit:
https://www.nps.gov/thrb/learn/historyculture/storyofteddybear.htm

Important Teddy Bear Dates:
National Teddy Bear Day is September 9.
National Bring Your Teddy To Work/School Day is observed on the second Wednesday of October.
Teddy Bear Picnic Day is July 10.

For FREE Teddy Bear Tea educational activities and lessons visit:
www.ellwynautumn.com.

Other books by Ellwyn Autumn

The Kamyla Chung Series:
Kamyla Chung and the Creepy-Crawlies
Kamyla Chung and the Classroom Bully

CPSIA information can be obtained
at www.ICGtesting.com
Printed in the USA
LVIC061046080920
665109LV00007B/30